This Book Belongs To

Great Great Grandfather

Great Great Grandfather

Great Great Grandmother

Great Great Grandmother

Great Grandmother

Great Grandmother

Great Grandfather

Great Grandfather

Grandfather

Grandfather

Grandmother

Grandmother

Father

Mother

Family Tree

The Early
Days

What is your birthday?

_____

Where and when you Born? At home or in a hospital? Who delivered you?

_____

_____

_____

What was your full name at birth?

_____

_____

Was there anything unusual about your birth?

_____

_____

_____

Who named you? Does your name have any special meaning?

_____

_____

_____

Where are you named after a relative or someone else of significance?

_____

_____

In what city were you born?

_____

What was your height and weight at birth?

_____

_____

_____

What were your first words?

_____

_____

_____

Where are you easygoing? Did you cry easily?

_____

_____

_____

_____

How old were your parents when you were born?

_____

_____

_____

Were you the oldest middle or youngest child?

_____

_____

How many Siblings do you have?

_____

Were you the oldest middle youngest child for an only child?

_____

_____

How did your parents describe you as a baby?

_____

_____

_____

_____

What stories have you been told about the day you were born?

_____

_____

_____

_____

_____

What is a favorite childhood memory?

_____

_____

_____

_____

_____

_____

Childhood

Where did you grow up?

_____

_____

Do you have any nicknames? How did you get them?

_____

_____

_____

_____

What cities did you live in growing up?

_____

Did you grow up around brother and sister?

_____

_____

Describe them as true to someone who has never met them before?

_____

_____

What are your memories about the houses you lived in as a kid? Do you have a favorite?

_____

_____

_____

What did you have for play with as a child? That kids don't have today?

_____

_____

Who was your best friend?

_____

_____

What was your favorite toy or other item as a child?

_____

_____

Is there a television show you remember loving to wash?

_____

_____

What are your regular chores?

_____

_____

Did you get an allowance if yes how much?

_____

_____

_____

What do you miss most about being a kid?

_____

_____

_____

Why did you like it when you were a kid?

_____

_____

What was the worst trouble you remember getting into as a kid?

_____

_____

_____

What was your favorite Candy when you are a kid?

_____

Did you have a special blanket or stuffed animal?

_____

How would your presence describe your personality as a baby?

_____

_____

Is there any history about when you were a baby?

_____

_____

_____

What is your very first memory?

_____

_____

_____

What was your first wood?

_____

What was your first house like?

_____

_____

What was your room like?

_____

_____

What did a typical Meal time look like?

_____

_____

_____

What meals did you regularly eat growing up?

_____

_____

_____

What things did you not have as a child that we have today?

_____

_____

_____

What was your relationship like with your siblings? Cousin? Friends?

_____

_____

_____

Who was your first Crush? Did he/she like you back?

_____

_____

_____

What did you think of your first school dance?

_____

_____

_____

What was your proudest moment as a child?

_____

_____

_____

_____

What was your relationship like with your mom?

_____

_____

_____

What was your relationship like with your dad?

_____

_____

_____

What special treats, meals, snacks or other food did your family eat?

_____

_____

_____

_____

What holidays did you celebrate and how did you celebrate them?

_____

_____

_____

Where did you go on satiation or vacation as a child?

_____

_____

_____

Did you travel as a child? What were your favorite places to visit?

_____

_____

_____

_____

Teenage Years

How did you dress and style your hair during your tense? Do you have any pictures?

_____

_____

_____

What is your happiest moment as a teenager? Your saddest?

_____

_____

_____

Did you hang out with a group of people or a small number of close friends? Are any of you still in contact?

_____

_____

_____

_____

Did you have any girlfriends in your teen years?

_____

_____

What music did you like as a teenager?

_____

_____

What was a common weekend night for you during your teens?

_____

_____

_____

Did you have a curfew?

_____

_____

In what kind of car did you learn to drive?

_____

_____

_____

Knowing all you know now what advice would you give your teenage self?

_____

_____

_____

Describe what you wear like during your teen years?

_____

_____

_____

How did you celebrate Christmas when you were young?

_____

_____

_____

What made you the most nervous during your teenage years?

_____

_____

_____

What sports or other extracurricular activities where you involved in?

_____

_____

_____

_____

What did you most excel at as a child/teen/high school student?

_____

_____

_____

Did you go to college or get additional training after high school? Where did you go? What did you study/get trained in?

_____

_____

_____

_____

_____

_____

_____

How would you describe a perfect day when you were young?

_____

_____

_____

_____

_____

_____

_____

_____

_____

_____

_____

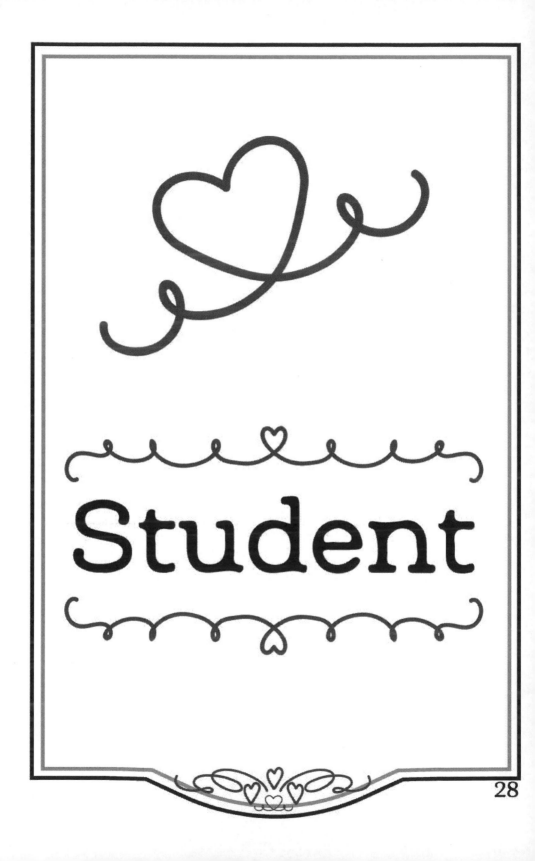

Student

28

Did you enjoy school?

_____

_____

What kind of student were you?

_____

_____

_____

What would you do for fun?

_____

_____

What schools did you attend?

_____

_____

What were your favorite subjects?

_____

_____

Who was your favorite school teacher? Why?

_____

_____

_____

_____

How would your classmates remember you?

_____

_____

_____

_____

Are you still friends with anyone from that time in your life?

_____

_____

What are your best memories of grade school/high school/college/graduate school?
Worst memories?

_____

_____

_____

_____

_____

_____

_____

_____

Was there a teacher or teachers who had a particularly strong influence on your life? Tell me about them.

Do you have any favorite stories from school?

Who were your friends throughout your life?
What did you do with them?

_____

_____

_____

_____

_____

_____

_____

_____

_____

_____

Love & Marriage

Do you have a love of your life? When did you first fall in love?

_____

_____

_____

_____

_____

How did you propose?

_____

_____

_____

_____

_____

_____

Did you date in High School? What was your first date?

_____

_____

_____

_____

_____

Do you believe in love at first sight?

_____

_____

_____

_____

_____

_____

What lessons have you learned from your relationships?

_____

_____

_____

_____

_____

_____

_____

_____

_____

_____

Do you remember your first date?
Do you remember the best date you ever went on?

How did you meet your spouse/partner?

_____

_____

_____

When and how did you know that your future spouse/partner was "the one"?

_____

_____

_____

_____

_____

_____

_____

What were the best times? The most difficult times?

Did you ever think of getting divorced?

_____

_____

_____

What was your wedding day like?

_____

_____

_____

_____

_____

_____

_____

Do you have any favorite stories from your marriage or about your spouse/partner?

Adulthood

Who inspired you as you matured?

_____

_____

what did your parents do for work?

_____

_____

_____

What was your first job? How old were you? What did you do?
How much did you get paid?

_____

_____

_____

_____

Describe the work that you do? Do you like your job?

_____

_____

_____

_____

_____

How has faith/spirituality/religion/meditation played a role in your life?

_____

_____

_____

_____

_____

Do you have any favorite stories from your work life?

How has exercise (sports/dance/yoga/etc) played a role in your life?

_____

_____

_____

_____

_____

How have service and charity played a role in your life?

_____

_____

_____

_____

_____

How would you describe your personality?

_____

_____

_____

What are your greatest strengths?

_____

_____

_____

What is your greatest weakness?

_____

_____

_____

_____

Are you an introvert or an extrovert?

_____

_____

_____

How did you balance work and home life?

_____

_____

_____

_____

_____

_____

_____

Parenting

When did you first find out that you'd be a parent? How did you feel?

_____

_____

_____

_____

_____

Did you want a big or a small family? How many kids did you have?

_____

_____

_____

_____

_____

What are your memories about expecting your first child?

_____

_____

_____

_____

What are your memories about the birth of your first child?

_____

_____

_____

_____

_____

Did you always know you wanted to be a parent?

_____

_____

_____

_____

Can you describe the moment when you saw your child for the first time?

_____

_____

_____

_____

_____

_____

_____

How has being a parent changed you?

_____

_____

_____

_____

What have you learned about yourself from being a parent?

_____

_____

_____

_____

_____

_____

What are your dreams for your children?

_____

_____

_____

_____

_____

_____

Do you remember when your last child left home for good?

_____

_____

_____

_____

_____

What was your happiest memory about being a first time parent?

_____

_____

_____

_____

_____

_____

_____

_____

_____

_____

_____

What has been the most fun part about parenting?

_____

_____

_____

_____

What has been the hardest thing about parenting?

_____

_____

_____

_____

_____

_____

_____

Do you have any favorite stories about your kids?

Favorites

What are your memories about the houses you lived in as a kid?

_____

_____

_____

_____

What was your favorite activity?

_____

_____

_____

_____

_____

_____

_____

What were your favorite hobbies?

_____

_____

What was your favorite place? What were your favorite places to visit?

_____

_____

_____

_____

What was your favorite food? Why?

_____

_____

_____

_____

What was your favorite Color?

_____

What was your favorite game?

_____

Who were your favorite relatives?

_____

_____

What was your favorite Candy?

_____

_____

What was your favorite music and movies?

_____

_____

Tell about your most memorable birthday?

_____

_____

_____

_____

_____

How did you typically celebrate your birthday?

_____

_____

_____

_____

_____

Tell about your favorite holiday memory?

_____

_____

_____

_____

What holidays did you celebrate and how did you celebrate them?

_____

_____

_____

_____

_____

What was your favorite pet like your child?

_____

_____

What special treats, meals, snacks or other food did your family eat?

_____

_____

_____

_____

_____

_____

_____

What is your favorite story?

Family Tree

Where are your parents' families from?

_____

_____

Have you ever been there? What was that experience like?

_____

_____

_____

_____

What traditions have been passed down in your family?

_____

_____

_____

_____

When did they come to this country and why?

_____

_____

_____

_____

_____

Where did they settle and what did they do there?

_____

_____

_____

_____

What tourists do you know about them?

_____

_____

_____

_____

_____

Do you have any objects that belonged to an ancestor?

_____

_____

_____

_____

_____

Do you know any e relatives who speak a language other than English?

_____

_____

Who was the oldest relative you know? What do you remember most about this person?

_____

_____

_____

_____

_____

_____

_____

_____

Who is the most famous person in your family?
Who is considered the most admired for the most interesting relative
are they any e "Black Sheep"?

How did you and grandma/grandpa meet?

_____

_____

_____

_____

Who is the best history seller in your family? What does this person talk about?

_____

_____

_____

_____

_____

_____

Do you remember any of the stories they used to tell you?

What are the classic family stories? Jokes? Songs?

_____

_____

_____

_____

_____

_____

_____

_____

_____

_____

_____

Do you remember any of the stories your grandparents used to tell you?

How would you like to be remembered?

_____

_____

_____

_____

_____

_____

_____

_____

_____

_____

What were your parents like?

_____

_____

_____

_____

_____

_____

_____

_____

_____

_____

What were your grandparents like?

Tell about your grandparents?

Tell about your parents?

_____

_____

_____

_____

_____

_____

_____

_____

_____

_____

Tell about your aunts?

_____

_____

_____

_____

_____

_____

_____

_____

_____

_____

_____

Tell about your uncles?

_____

_____

_____

_____

_____

_____

_____

_____

_____

_____

Tell about your cousins?

_____

_____

_____

_____

_____

_____

_____

_____

_____

_____

_____

Are there any funny stories your family tells about you that come to mind?

Feeling And Emotion

What are you most proud of as an child?

_____

_____

_____

_____

_____

What are you most proud of as an adult?

_____

_____

_____

_____

_____

First income of your life?

_____

_____

What a joy it was to be the first Parent in life?

_____

_____

_____

_____

_____

_____

_____

_____

Can you tell me about the important people in your life?

What have been some of the happiest moments in your life? The saddest?

Can you tell me about a moment when a person's kindness made a difference in your life?

_____

_____

_____

_____

_____

_____

_____

_____

_____

_____

_____

What is your earliest memory?

_____

_____

_____

_____

_____

_____

_____

_____

_____

_____

_____

How would you like to be remembered?

Is there anything that you've never told me but want to tell me now?

Express Yourself

What did you look like?

_____

_____

_____

_____

_____

What are the most important lessons you've learned in life?

_____

_____

_____

_____

_____

What was the best part of your 20s?

_____

_____

_____

_____

What was the best part of your 30s?

_____

_____

_____

_____

_____

Who has been the biggest influence on your life?
What lessons did that person or those people teach you?

_____

_____

_____

_____

_____

_____

_____

_____

_____

_____

_____

What has been your proudest professional achievement?

_____

_____

_____

_____

_____

_____

_____

_____

_____

_____

_____

What has been your proudest personal achievement?

If you could have a do over, what would you Change?

_____

_____

_____

_____

_____

_____

_____

_____

_____

_____

_____

Advice
And
Final Thought

What advice would you give your younger self?

_____

_____

_____

_____

_____

_____

_____

_____

_____

_____

_____

What advice would you give to your teenage children/grandchildren?

_____

_____

_____

_____

_____

What advice would you give to your single adult children/grandchildren?

_____

_____

_____

_____

_____

What advice do you have for young couples?

What advice would you give to your married children/grandchildren regarding dear marital relationships?

_____

_____

_____

_____

What advice would you give to your married children/grandchildren regarding parenting?

_____

_____

_____

_____

_____

What advice would you give to any of your children/grandchildren regarding life in general?

_____

_____

_____

_____

_____

What legacy would you like to be known for?

_____

_____

_____

_____

_____

What was on your bucket list when you were younger?

_____

_____

_____

_____

_____

How has your bucket list changed as you have grown older?

_____

_____

_____

_____

_____

If you could only do three more things on your bucket list, what would they be? why?

What Life lesson helped you grow the very most? how? why?

What is something that people don't know about you?

How do you imagine your death?

_____

_____

_____

_____

_____

Do you believe in an after-life?

_____

_____

_____

_____

Do you have any last wishes?

_____

_____

_____

_____

_____

_____

_____

_____

_____

_____

How do you want to be remembered?

Remembering
A
Loved One

What is your best memory of ___?

_____

_____

_____

What is your most vivid memory of ___?

_____

_____

_____

What did ___ mean to you?

_____

_____

_____

_____

Are you comfortable/ can you talk about ____'s death?

_____

_____

_____

What has been the hardest thing about losing ____?

_____

_____

_____

What would you ask ____ if ____ were here today?

_____

_____

_____

What do you miss most about ____?

_____

_____

_____

How do you think ____ would want to be remembered?

_____

_____

_____

Can you talk about the biggest obstacles ____ overcame in life?

_____

_____

_____

_____

What about ____ makes you smile?

_____

_____

_____

Did you have any favorite jokes ____ used to tell?

_____

_____

_____

_____

What were ____'s hopes and dreams for the future?

_____

_____

_____

Is there something about ____ that you think no one else knows?

_____

_____

_____

How are you different now than you were before you lost ____?

_____

_____

_____

_____

What is the image of ____ that persists?

_____

_____

_____

Do you have any traditions to honor _____?

_____

_____

_____

_____

_____

What has helped you the most in your grief_____?

_____

_____

_____

_____

_____

What are the hardest times ____?

Notes

PHOTO